Reminiscence
WITH ELDERLY PEOPLE

for Alison and Matthew

First published in 1986 by
Winslow Press,
Telford Road, Bicester, Oxon OX6 0TS
Reprinted 1988

ISBN 0 86388 041 X

02-147   Printed in Great Britain by
Hobbs the Printers, Southampton

CONTENTS

CHAPTER 1

WHAT IS REMINISCING?

eminiscing is something we have all probably spent some of our lives doing. Literally speaking, to reminisce means to recall memories of past events. And yet, from our own experience of reminiscing, we are probably aware that it is something more than just thinking or talking about the past. When we reminisce, we do not recall any random event in a cold, factual way but we bring to mind the experiences that are personal to us in a vivid and alive fashion.

Reminiscing about personal events can involve a variety of senses including recall of sounds, smells, tastes, and touch as well as recapturing visual scenes. Reminiscing can be associated with and trigger off a wide variety of emotions from happiness to sadness, anger to joy and grief to elation.

Reminiscing then, is a rich experience distinguished from the memory of less personal events by the fact that it involves the process of reliving the past rather than of factual recall of historical events. Indeed, one of the distinctive features about our reminiscences is how they colour the past in a way which often best suits ourselves. We are all familiar with the fisherman's tale about his prize catch which gets bigger each time he tells his story. This is but one example of how we each remember events according to our personal experience of them and not necessarily of how they occurred in reality. Reminiscing is a process which focuses on the personal way we experience and remember events rather than on chronological, historical or factual accuracy.

Of course not all our reminiscing is done in public or in conversation with others. Sometimes a particular sound or the sight of a particular scene may trigger off a train of private thought which takes us through a whole chain of memories which we daydream about or contemplate individually. So it is not always obvious to others when someone is reminiscing. However this in no way devalues the experience of the individual. And although in this book we shall be concentrating on ways of encouraging older people to share their reminiscences and the consequent benefits thereof, we should not forget how equally important private reminiscing can be, especially to the confused old person who finds it difficult to communicate with others.

SUMMARY
Reminiscing:
- can involve a variety of senses and emotions
- reflects the personal way we remember things
- can be 'public' or 'private'

CHAPTER 2

THE ROLE OF REMINISCING
IN OLD AGE

Reminiscence is as old as history itself and we all have the ability to reminisce as soon as we become aware that we have a memory. And so, in every sense, reminiscing is a natural and universally occurring process.

In spite of the fact that we all reminisce, looking back at the past is something that has become associated with old age. The problem is that it has often been seen as an inevitable consequence of old age when people are forced to concentrate on the past perhaps because of difficulties in coping with increasing frailty in the present. This view is misleading, not only because a good proportion of people labelled as old lead very active, fit and healthy lives, but also it ignores the positive aspects that the wisdom and experience of older people, reflected in their reminiscences, can contribute to life.

There are also a number of ways in which reminiscing can help the elderly person and others adapt to or come to terms with growing older.

Reminiscing can serve as a means of highlighting the assets of older people rather

3

than their disabilities. For instance, even though a person might become less quick at making decisions or increasingly forgetful of recent events as they get older, often their memory for events further in their past remains extremely good. Thus reminiscing can help to maintain older people's self esteem by focusing on the things they *can* do rather than confronting them with what they cannot do.

Reminiscing can enhance feelings of self worth by providing an opportunity for old people to share the wisdom and experience they have accumulated through their lives with others. In more ancient, tribal cultures it was the responsibility of the village elder to pass on the wisdom of one generation to the next.

This role, which was the province of the old person, has been eroded in our own society by the advent of books and the media. Providing the opportunity for older people to share their reminiscences can help to compensate for this.

Reminiscing can also help the older person to retain a sense of individual identity and aid in conveying this to others. Many elderly people are the victims of a rather negative stereotype thrust upon them by those who have had little or no contact with their generation. This stereotype depicts the typical old person as someone who is physically disabled, confused, dependent and sometimes even a vegetable. An opportunity to share the old person's unique collection of personal experiences can help to dispel this stereotype and show him as a real individual.

It has also been suggested that reminiscence plays a vital role in the process of life review. The term life review was first coined by Robert Butler who suggested that all people coming near to the end of their lives, and therefore old people in particular, become involved in a process of looking back over their lives in an attempt to identify and come to terms with events which were unresolved at the time they occurred eg. significant losses, grief reactions, guilt complexes, etc. Butler suggests that this life review process is a sort of psychological preparation for death and forms a part of the natural process of human development as a person gets older. Reminiscing then may be the means by which the material for the life review process is generated and as such forms part of the means by which people are able to take on board their old age and coming to the end of their lives.

Finally, and probably most importantly, as anyone who has spent time listening to an old person talking about their past will know, reminiscing can be a stimulating and enjoyable experience. For many older people, the opportunities to become involved in appropriate social activities can be limited and so it is important that what opportunities they do have are as rewarding as possible. Reminiscing, because it relies on those experiences which are relevant to the individual, provides the best opportunities for this to happen.

SUMMARY

Reminiscence is a universal experience that can be of particular importance to older people because:

- it highlights their assets rather than their disabilities.
- it can enhance their feelings of self worth and esteem.
- it can help in recognising individuality and identity.
- it can aid in the life review process.
- it is enjoyable and stimulating!

CHAPTER 3

REMINISCENCE IN HOMES AND HOSPITALS FOR THE ELDERLY

We have just considered the role that reminiscence can have in helping to enhance the individual identity of the elderly person. The significance of this aspect of reminiscing is nowhere more important than for the small minority of people who are found to need long-term care in a residential home for the elderly or hospital ward.

Not only does the old person have to leave behind many aspects of a world which he has spent a lifetime gathering and creating around him, but he also finds himself confronted with a totally new lifestyle consisting of unfamiliar people, unfamiliar places and unfamiliar routines. The danger is that the person can get lost in a crowd and lose his identity.

On top of the disability which had necessitated his coming into care in the first place, this process of depersonalisation can tempt the new long-stay resident to withdraw in such a way that his individuality becomes further obscured. This means that staff, who can often find very little time away from the many demands of providing physical care to get to know their residents anyway, can sometimes

7

lose sight of the person as an individual.

The result of all this can be that the old person becomes depressed, withdrawn and isolated. Indeed, failure to take into account the individual needs of residents can sometimes give rise to additional problems for the staff. For instance, a resident who is lonely may resort to shouting or urinating in inappropriate places to gain the staff's attention. Likewise the resident who has always been particular about cleanliness may become resistant or unco-operative if staff try to take over his bathing or washing.

From this we can see how important it is for staff to become familiar with their residents, their backgrounds and their lifestyles. For a resident, recognition as an individual can help to overcome the traumatic transition of coming into care and in maintaining the quality of life in the new environment once they are there. This becomes all the more important for the person who is unable to communicate easily — for the confused old person or the person whose speech has been affected by a stroke.

Also, in the long-term care situation, the reminiscences of elderly residents can serve as a reminder to the staff of the individuality of each old person they are looking after. In providing time to listen to these reminiscences, staff are also communicating to the residents that they acknowledge and recognise the importance of their lives in spite of the disability which has necessitated their admission into long-term care.

Furthermore, as we shall be describing in more detail, if the elderly residents' reminiscences, and hence their personal lifestyles, form the basis on which the care regime and recreational activities are organised, the residents are provided with a means of making an active contribution to life in the home or hospital ward. This can help the elderly to feel more positive about themselves and to feel that they have something worthwhile and useful to offer.

Many old people resent always being the object of other people's charity or having no control over the pattern of their lives. Making this contribution allows the elderly resident a break from being placed in a dependent or 'cared for' role.

SUMMARY
Acknowledging the importance of the reminiscences of old people in long-term care:
- can help to reduce the trauma of admission
- can help to recognise them as individuals with a separate past and lifestyle
- puts other disabilities in perspective
- provides a means by which they can have some influence over their own lives in the hospital and/or home.

CHAPTER 4

ENCOURAGING REMINISCENCE

With many older people, if you put aside enough time and ask the right questions, they will sit and talk for hours about themselves and their past. Indeed, the problem usually comes when you try and get them to stop! Such is the importance reminiscence has to play in the lives of the elderly.

Nevertheless it may be difficult to encourage some old people to share their memories. This might be for a variety of reasons. For instance, it might be that you have caught them on the wrong day. It may be that you have asked the wrong questions or the person finds it difficult to remember.

In this chapter we are going to look at several ways in which reminiscence can be used to establish rapport and communication between old people and others. However, a word of warning. Although a heavy emphasis has already been laid on the role that reminiscing can play in improving the quality of life for the elderly and in helping them to adjust to their old age, over and above all this, we must remember the individual's right to privacy, their choice not to share things they wish to keep to themselves. We may feel that to share an upsetting memory or to have things out in the open may be in the person's own interests, but, if our aims in encouraging reminiscence are to promote individuality and self-worth for the old person, we must respect his or her right to remain silent as part of that process. That is not to say every time difficulties arise or the old person gets upset, we should immediately back away. On the contrary this may be the very time when sensitive encouragement would be of immense value. This is something we shall discuss further in chapter 6. But for the moment, we should bear in mind that encouraging an elderly person to reminisce must go hand in hand with sensitivity and recognition of what that person wants to do. Let's take a look at some of the different contexts in which old people can be encouraged to reminisce.

Reminiscence on a one-to-one basis

The most important feature of the old person's reminiscences are that they are unique to that individual. Their memories represent the accumulation of a wealth of experience — the people they have met, the places they have been, the things they have done and so on. Coupled with the multitude of ways in which we remember our personal experiences, the result is a complex web of memories held together only by the life of the person who has gathered them. To communicate the extent and depth of these experiences to another person is therefore, in one sense, an impossible task. And so the only hope of beginning to understand the individual in the context of their past is to spend time with them on a one-to-one basis.

This kind of situation is a very powerful one. First of all, there is the opportunity for strong rapport to develop between reminiscer and listener. Mutual trust can be built up and a wide range of experiences can be shared. The very existence of a one-to-one relationship in which the old person is provided with the opportunity to reminisce can powerfully communicate a recognition of the identity and importance of the individual. The one-to-one relationship allows better opportunity for the listener to adapt to the pace and the whim of the reminiscer. More time is available to ascertain and develop those themes on the individual's past which seem to be of particular importance. The one-to-one situation also provides more time for those who find it less easy to share themselves in the company of others.

A one-to-one situation then is a highly personalised opportunity for an old person and an interested listener to develop a strong rapport and mutual trust. The pace and the content of the reminiscences can also be more easily adapted to the individual.

Reminiscing in groups

From a practical point of view, particularly in old people's homes or hospitals, there may not always be enough time to devote to one-to-one reminiscence sessions. In these situations it may be appropriate to bring together small groups of elderly people to share their reminiscences. This has the advantage that the memories of one old person may help to trigger off the memories of other members of the group. The group then becomes self-perpetuating and motivated by the contributions of its members.

Reminiscence groups can also provide a useful social forum in which old people can meet and get to know one another. This can be particularly important in homes or hospital wards for the elderly where the only thing people may have in common are aspects of their past. World events, eg. the wars, of which several people may have had experience, can be good starting points for building up relationships between elderly people who might otherwise be strangers. Alternatively the groups themselves can provide an opportunity for things common to the lives of several members to emerge so helping to establish links between them.

Reminiscence groups then, are a way of bringing old people together in a social setting so that they can get to know each other and pursue common interests. In chapter 6 we shall look at how reminiscence groups operate in more detail.

Not all reminiscing has to take place in prescribed situations. In practice this will not happen anyway because old people inevitably drift into talking about their past at various points throughout the day and as an incidental part of their contact with other people. So part of encouraging reminiscing, and what it represents, is recognising and giving due space and respect to a person's reminiscences whenever they occur. In a ward or a home, this may be when the person is being bathed or taken to the toilet. It may be that a special occasion or a particular meal triggers off memories about the person's past. Elderly persons in their own homes may be prompted to reminiscence simply as a result of a friend calling to do the shopping. Whatever the situation, the important thing is that the listener is receptive. This will then provide the necessary encouragement for old people to share more about themselves.

Recognition of the importance of reminiscence can also be affected by the kind of environment in which the old person is cared for. So, for instance, encouraging a new elderly resident to bring personal photographs and belongings at the time of his admission may be a way of recognising and helping him to maintain

Reminiscence as an integral part of care

links with his past. Likewise, a residential home or hospital ward which has pictures to which residents can relate eg. posters from the war, displayed on the wall may provide an acknowledgement of the importance of their background and lifestyle.

SUMMARY

Reminiscing can be encouraged:
- on a one-to-one basis, where more time is available to adapt to an individual.
- in groups, where old people can share their memories.
- as part of care, by recognising its importance throughout the day and in all environments.

CHAPTER 5

REMINISCENCE AIDS

*O*ne of the distinguishing features of reminiscing is that the memory of one event often triggers off memories of others. This process continues until we find ourselves reviewing a whole chain of events from our past. Anything can act as the initial trigger — a photograph, a sound, something that is said and so on. The important feature of a trigger is that it usually bears some relation or resemblance to an event or experience from our past. These triggers can often act as a useful aid to encouraging reminiscing. For older people in particular it may be necessary to provide prompts or memory joggers to help bring recollections of the past more readily to mind.

What makes a good reminiscence aid?

As we have said, the most important characteristic of a reminiscence trigger is its relevance to the individual or group for whom it is intended. Thus there is little or no point in showing a farmer, who lived in the countryside during the war, pictures of underground railway stations being used as air raid shelters. Neither will playing songs from the First World War be likely to produce much response from someone who was born in the 1920s. Reminiscence

triggers must bear relevance to the individual's
- age
- background
- lifestyle and
- experience.

With elderly people whose sight or hearing may be poor, it is important to ensure that the triggers or stimulus material are clear and distinctive in the way they relate to the subject concerned. For instance, abstract art impressions of past events have less value in stimulating reminiscence than actual photographs — unless the reminiscer is an art connoisseur! It will be important to relate the kind of stimulation that a given trigger provides to the reminiscer's
- abilities
- personality and
- mental capacity.

Thus, for a frail or mentally alert group of people, scenes depicting different aspects of an experience may be helpful in prompting a variety of reminiscences. For the highly distractible or confused old person, however, triggers with just one theme may prove to be the most effective.

We have noted how reminiscing is a process which involves all the senses. In the same way reminiscence triggers can utilise all the senses. Indeed, if the maximum benefit is to be derived from a reminiscence trigger, it should involve as many different kinds of senses as possible. Objects or personal mementos are a good example of triggers that can prompt reminiscence through a variety of means. The texture or smell of an object can have just as much reminiscence potential as what it looks like. Combined together, a powerful reminiscence aid is created.

Bearing in mind the factors we have mentioned above, the number and variety of aids to reminiscence are limited only by the imagination. Because a person's life is made up of a huge diversity of experiences remembered in a wide variety of ways the potential resources available for reminiscence triggers are enormous.

Some possible reminiscence aids

One of the aids available is *Nostalgia*. This series of reminiscence aids consists of stimulus cards on particular topics, eg. domestic objects and vehicles from the past to the present and banner headlines and royalty from the earlier part of this century. Remembering the 20s, 30s and 40s are photo packs in the *Bygone Decades* series which focus on everyday scenes from that decade. Another example is *Recall* which is a series of six tapes/slide sequences depicting scenes which a typical Londoner might have seen over the past eighty years.

Other aids to reminiscence that have been particularly successful are *Reminiscence Theatre* and *Reminiscence Outings*. In *Reminiscence Theatre* groups of players enact typical scenes from the past eg. music hall scenes, a munitions factory, etc. using the information given to them through the reminiscences of elderly people, or sometimes by involving them in the drama itself. This can be a particularly powerful reminiscence trigger because of the active participation and involvement of the old person in the process. Similarly, *Reminiscence Outings*, planned on the basis of participants' experience of places and events remembered, can be an effective way of stimulating memories.

Other ideas include the use of personal mementos, photographs, *Memory Diary*, magazines, comics, etc. For more details of these and other suggestions of reminiscence aids see Appendices II and III.

Again, we should emphasise that the best indicator of a good reminiscence aid is the impact it has on the individual and its effectiveness in producing a response.

Using reminiscence aids

It is very tempting, having acquired or created appropriate reminiscence aids to want to let them loose on the elderly person straight away. However the results are likely to be disappointing if a few basic tips are not taken into consideration.

Too much information. Firstly, it is important not to bombard the old person with too much stimulus material at once.

It is worth remembering that as people get older it may take them longer to respond to a trigger and therefore they must be given time. Apart from crowding the old person, providing too much material may confuse them.

Use of cues. For some old people, it may be necessary to offer cues or prompts about the material presented to them.

For instance, the presenter might introduce material by making some descriptive remarks to help the old person orientate themselves towards the subject matter eg. of a coronation picture the presenter might say "Let's have a look at this photograph of a member of the royal family". This might be followed by a question or prompt focussing on one aspect of the stimulus material and then trying to relate it to the individual's personal experience eg. "Do you know who this is? . . . What were you doing at the time of the coronation?".

Relating personal experience. As we noted earlier, the important feature of reminiscing is that it gives the person the opportunity to relate his personal experience of events.

It follows that in presenting stimulus

material we should not be seeking to extract factual accounts of events. Instead, it is the individual's perception of those events that is important.

Related experiences. Finally, just as one memory triggers off a whole chain of others, so a given piece of stimulus material may spark off any number of reminiscences.

For this reason there is no point in confining the reminiscer to the particular topic or event suggested by the content of the stimulus material. Indeed, it may be that the theme which the material suggests to the presenter is not the same as the memories triggered off in the reminiscer. It is important therefore that the presenter of reminiscence triggers takes the lead from the old person he is involved with.

Reminiscence *aids* are just that. They are a means to an end which involves the old person giving of himself.

SUMMARY

A good aid to reminiscence is one that is:
- appropriate to the age, background, experience and lifestyle of the old person
- tailored to the abilities of the individual
- involves as many senses as possible.
  Reminiscence aids:

- should not be overused or used too quickly
- may require prompts and cues
- should facilitate recall of personal experiences, not historical accuracy
- should facilitate a range of reminiscences and not limit them.

CHAPTER 6

REMINISCENCE GROUPS

*W*e have already suggested some of the advantages of bringing elderly people together in reminiscence groups. In this chapter we shall look in more detail at how these groups can be set up, how to run groups effectively, the role of the group leader and some of the difficulties that might be encountered.

The first thing to determine when setting up a reminiscence group is what its function is intended to be. In chapter 2 we suggested a number of functions which reminiscing might have for an old person and any or all of these can be reflected in the way a reminiscence group is run.

Type of group

Generally speaking reminiscence groups can operate on three levels:

1. As a recreational activity — where the emphasis is on providing occupation or leisure activities for the elderly.
2. As a psychological support — where the reminiscing is directed toward generating self-esteem and expressing individual identity.
3. As a therapy tool — where the focus is

on aiding the life review process and helping the elderly person to adjust to later life.

It is vital to decide what kind of group is to be run *before* it is set up because this will influence some of the other decisions that have to be made. For instance, if a reminiscence group is set up solely as a recreational activity then it will be less important to restrict the number of people in the group. On the other hand, groups which are designed to help their members explore very personal and highly emotionally charged issues will need to be made more intimate.

Each of the three kinds of groups mentioned above is valid in its own right. In practice, the function of the group may move among the different levels, but it is still important to have a clear idea about the kind of group it seems appropriate to run and which the group leader will feel comfortable about being involved in. In the same way, it is important that elderly people being invited to join a reminiscence group know exactly what to expect.

Planning the group structure

Number of members

We have found the optimum number of participants in a group is between 5 and 8, providing there are at least two group leaders. Any more than this then the group becomes unwieldy and allows only occasional and superficial contributions from each group member. Any less than this number and the opportunity for sharing and exchanging memories with other people becomes limited.

Frequency of the group

For a group to establish cohesion and its own identity it should meet at least once a week and preferably more often where people with poor memory are involved. Reminiscence groups, like any groups, can be draining for both leaders and participants and therefore it is useful to plan sessions to run in a series of six to ten. These blocks of sessions can then be followed by a couple of weeks' break to allow time for a rest, a review and, where appropriate, to make plans for the next block.

Length of session

Obviously the most important thing to take into consideration when planning how long each session should last is the concentration span of the participants. Forty-five minutes usually seems right as a maximum, but the actual length will depend on who is involved and what form the reminiscence activity takes; for example it is easier to hold someone's attention with films or objects than it is just by sitting and talking. Remember, it will be necessary to be flexible as, like us all, old people also have their off days.

Selecting group members

The most important factor for potential group members is compatibility. This may be measured in terms of age, sex, background, lifestyle, mental ability or intelligence level. Whatever dimension is used, some attempt must be made to ascertain how likely the people who are selected for the group will complement each other and the intended function of the group. For instance, there will be little point in having one quiet and withdrawn resident in a group which is designed to be a self-perpetuating form of light entertainment. Either that person will drag the group down or he will be excluded from the group altogether.

Role of the group leader

In one sense, the term 'Group Leader' can be misleading if taken to imply that one person has to take charge of and/or direct the group in the way he/she wants it to go. For as we have already seen, this could well be contrary to the rationale of a reminiscence group which is intended to encourage the group members to take responsibility for the direction of the sessions by relating *their* personal experiences. Bearing this in mind, there are a number of

28

roles a group leader might have to take on in a reminiscence group to ensure that the group functions reasonably well.

The interested listener

First and foremost the group leader must show himself to be someone who is ready, willing and able to listen and respect the contributions of the group members. Only if a receptive atmosphere is created will members be encouraged to share of themselves. We have seen that an essential part of the reminiscing process is that the reminiscer can give of him/herself and that this contribution will be taken seriously. Without providing a detailed description of listening skills, we know that the willingness of a leader to listen can be conveyed in many ways, eg. by making encouraging remarks, nodding, appropriate eye gaze, smiling and so on.

The facilitator

In those groups where people find it difficult or are reluctant to share their memories, the group leader may have to prompt or cue some response. This can be done by asking open-ended questions, providing stimulus material and by picking up on any responses which are offered.

The pupil/partner

An essential feature of reminiscence is its role in enabling the old person to pass on their specific expertise and experience to others. At times, the group leader may be a partner in exploring memories with the elderly people. At other times, the leader may take on the role of pupil, sitting back and allowing the old person to teach him from his store of memories.

The pacemaker

The group leader will be responsible for ensuring the amount of time spent on any one particular topic is such that the group members neither miss their chance to make their contribution, nor become bored by over kill. The group leader will also be responsible for ensuring that new stimulus material is provided at the right point in each session.

The supporter

There will be times in some group sessions when individual members of the group find it difficult to share a particular memory or find it upsetting to do so. While the individual's right to privacy must be preserved at all costs, in some cases gentle, sensitive encouragement and support may be appropriate to help the person to face and share particularly difficult issues. This is an additional function the group leader may have to fulfill — when he may have to decide whether the sensitive areas are something which the other group members and the group leader himself can handle. Where it seems an individual needs to share an upsetting event and this appears inappropriate in the group setting, arrangements may have to be made to follow this up with the person concerned, after the group is over.

The co-ordinator

Another task the group leader may have to take on is that of ensuring that everyone gets a reasonable opportunity to participate in the group. This means holding back the more dominant members of the group, and at the same time trying to bring out the quieter members. It also means ensuring that the contribution of one member is picked up by the other members and it can be a specific task of the leader to relate specific themes which do arise to all the members of the group.

As with any group, there will be times when a particular session does not run as well as others. This may be a result of a lack of response from members or because the leader has to do a lot of work to get any interaction between members at all. In this section we shall briefly look at three areas of difficulty often encountered in reminiscence groups.

Problems in running reminiscence groups

Group members do not talk about the past

Sometimes group members will wander away from their own recollections of the past and start to make comparisons with the present. This is wholly appropriate because it reflects the role that reminiscence has in linking the elderly person's past with the present and thus helping him to adjust to later life.

Members' reminiscences become confused with reality

This can take two forms. Firstly, group members may distort or exaggerate their past. However, we have already mentioned that this is a typical feature of reminiscences and unless it causes conflict for the reminiscer or others in the group, it should be accepted.

The second kind of confusion that arises is when memories of one event become muddled with those of another, for example World War I being confused with World War II. Where possible, it is useful to try and discover where the confusion lies providing this does not undermine the self-esteem of the reminiscer! Guiding members on to other topics may help in those cases where there is no point in trying to argue a case.

Group members become upset

The view that upsetting topics should be

avoided at all costs has been challenged already. Provided that the old person is willing and the leader feels able to explore these more sensitive areas then they should be encouraged. Sometimes avoidance of these areas reflects more of a difficulty on the part of the listener than it does of the reminiscer. For the latter, the chance to share an emotionally charged experience may be something which the person has had to wait a lifetime for. It can therefore be a highly appropriate function of reminiscence groups to do this.

As with any group, it is a good idea to have some means by which the group leaders can monitor how the group is going. This helps the leaders to identify both those factors which facilitate the good running of the group and those barriers which act as hurdles to its success. These success factors or barriers may lie within the composition of the group, the theme being discussed, the kind of stimulus material used, the skill of the leaders, and so on. The important thing is to be able to distinguish what makes a particular group function as it is.

Monitoring a reminiscence group

The means by which this monitoring can take place may be informal or carried out with the aid of a more structured assessment tool. For instance, where changes as a result of the group are dramatic and obvious, informal discussion and review after each group session may be sufficient (see below). Less dramatic changes may be observed by comparing participants' responses within the group with behaviour outside the group, or the responses between the group sessions using an observation scale such as that illustrated in Appendix VI. Again this kind of scale can be useful in determining the success and inhibiting factors which influence the running of a group.

In monitoring the group's progress, however, it should be remembered that changes may be slow and subtle in absolute terms but dramatic in the context of the rest of what the participants might be doing.

Maintaining the group

Once a a group is established it is essential that time and energy are put into ensuring that it continues to run for as long as it has value to the participants.

One of the biggest threats to the continuation of a group is when the factors which make the task of running the group more difficult fail to be identified. Thus it is important that at the end of each group session, time is put aside for the group leaders to carry out some kind of review of what has taken place. Just as important is that, periodically, the group has a break from meeting—this not only prevents burnout or boredom setting in, but also allows the leaders time to evaluate what has taken place and, where appropriate, plan for the next series of sessions.

It is often far better that leaders and participants commit themselves to a limited number of sessions and stop by mutual consent rather than a group outlives its usefulness and dies an uncomfortable death leaving everybody feeling demoralised. Regular reviews can help to prevent this.

SUMMARY

Reminiscence groups can be seen as:
- recreational activity
- psychological support
- therapy.

When setting up a group, special consideration needs to be given to:
- number of members in group
- frequency of meetings
- duration of meetings
- selection of group members.

The group leader may have to act as:
- an interested listener
- a facilitator
- a pupil/partner
- a pacemaker
- a supporter
- a co-ordinator.

Specific problems that may arise in reminiscence groups are when:

- members do not talk about the past
- members become confused about reality
- members become upset.

CHAPTER 7

BEYOND GROUP WORK

Reminiscence groups can be both a result and starting point for reminiscence based activities. We have already discussed how the group work situation facilitates the sharing of memories among old people but the contents of the reminiscence discussions may also be the inspiration for a whole range of other activities. In this chapter we shall look at some of the ways in which the content of reminiscences in group and other settings can form the basis on which other aspects of the old person's quality of life can be improved.

Reminiscence outings

Quite often, the reminiscences of old people refer to the places which have had a great impact on their lives. Places such as where a person was born, a street they used to live in, a school they attended, a park they played in, where they first met their spouse, to name a few, are often remembered quite vividly. When these places are still reasonably local, they can form the basis on which a route can be planned for outings for one or several old people. These kinds of outings can be tremendously stimulating for old people, not only because they provide a contrast from the four walls of the home or hospital in which they live, but also because revisiting places from their past can trigger off more memories from each person's range of experiences. Even when places revisited have changed from how they were when the person first knew them, memories may be sparked off of how things used to be and are thus instrumental in helping the old person to make links or comparisons between past and present.

Sometimes industrial firms or factories are happy to arrange for ex-employees to revisit their work place. This can have the added advantage of helping the old person to re-establish links with former colleagues and friends.

Other popular places to visit will be museums, antique shops and memorabilia exhibitions. Here, objects which were commonplace in the lives of older people in their younger days and which might be difficult to find, are readily accessible. These objects can act as a launching point for old people to pass on some wisdom from the past, experiences they have had and the way things used to be done.

For those old people living in institutional settings, admission to the home or hospital often coincides with severing of links with the community and their past. Reminiscence outings can help to re-establish or maintain these

links by facilitating contacts outside the institu-
tion.

Reminiscence outings have the potential to
fulfil many of the criteria for what makes a
good reminiscence aid as outlined in Chapter 5.
In particular, because the person is actively
participating in the outing, it means many, if
not all, the senses are stimulated. Moreover, the
reminiscence outing, planned on the basis of
individual participants' experience, is much
more likely to capture people's interest than
other kinds of trips.

Another way of helping old people in homes or
hospitals to maintain links with their past is by
ensuring that they or their relatives bring
personal belongings, objects and mementos of
personal significance when they are admitted.
Alternatively, local museums, antique shops or
historical societies may be prepared to lend
items of interest or relevance to the lives of
those residents. These objects can then be
arranged as a display or an exhibition by the
residents in such a way that they form a
physical reminder and environment in which,
literally speaking, the people feel at home.

Reminiscence displays

This kind of display often acts as a focus of
a talking point for visitors who, all too often,
find themselves at a loss for conversation when
they visit.

An exhibition produced by elderly people,

based on their experiences, can also be a useful attraction for school children as part of their history educat n.

In particular then, reminiscence displays can be a useful way of getting others involved in the experiences and pasts of elderly people. Not only can the setting up of the exhibition be a potentially stimulating, absorbing and enjoyable exercise for elderly residents, but the provision of objects for the displays may be a useful role which relatives or local groups would be welcome to undertake, and viewing the displays may be an attractive proposition for schools or other groups of people.

Recreational activity

Constructing reminiscence exhibitions and displays is one way of using the material from verbal reminiscence sessions to generate more physical activity and provide occupation during the day. Encouraging older people to talk about the leisure activities of their younger days may also generate ideas about recreational pastimes. It is all too easy to organise an activity such as Bingo or a Musical Sing-along because it seems like "a good idea", but if this kind of activity bears little significance or relevance to the lives and backgrounds of the people for whom it is intended then it is unlikely that much spontaneous enthusiasm is going to be raised. On the other hand, if the elderly residents are provided with the opportunity and choice to engage in more familiar pastimes, or share their knowledge of such pastimes with others, more response is likely to be evoked; eg, a game of "shove half-penny" may be more appropriate than "space invaders" for a member of the older generation.

Of course, other considerations such as the level of difficulty of the activity and the skills and abilities required, need to be taken into account when planning or facilitating activities for elderly people. The old person's reminiscences may provide clues about how familiar or appropriate activities are.

Another point worth bearing in mind is that people can participate in activities in a variety of ways. A game of bowls, for instance (especially adapted for indoors), requires not only players but also involves spectators, scorers and so on. Again, the most important consideration is the extent to which the kind of participation required of the individual is compatible with their background and interest. There is nothing worse than being coerced into an activity in which you have no interest.

Reminiscing then can provide the material or framework upon which a wide programme of activities can be planned. The success of such programmes is likely to depend on the extent to which the activities involve or reflect the interests, backgrounds and abilities of the people required to participate and the degree to which they feel involved in their organisation.

Institutional regime

Thus far we have concentrated on specific aspects of the lives of old people which can be positively influenced by taking into account their reminiscences. In chapter 4 we referred to the importance of taking the opportunities which the day-to-day routine of the home or hospital provides to encourage the old person to reminisce. In this section we want to highlight how the individual's background and past, as expressed through their reminiscences, can be used to influence the kind of life they lead in the present. This is not to be confused with encouraging the person to live in the past (see chapter 10); rather it is looking at ways in which a person's familiar lifestyle and hence the routines to which they have been accustomed throughout their lives, can be used as a basis for planning their daily routines. For instance, an elderly resident who used to be a farmer may have been accustomed to getting up at 4 o'clock each morning. To find himself in an old people's home where 7 o'clock is the prescribed rising time may be unnecessarily traumatic, and in some cases, may cause all sorts of problems including wandering, disturbed sleep, etc. Similarly many older people, particularly those living on their own, have been accustomed to making their midday meal the main meal of the day. These people might then find the three large meals often provided in institutions difficult to manage.

These are two examples of how institutional regimes may be incompatible with the lifestyle and/or background of individual residents. One of the positive consequences of trying to find out more about the individual and listening to their experiences is that it can provide suggestions as to how a whole variety of components of the daily routine can be adjusted and made compatible with the people being cared for. Appendix IV shows an example of the sort of information it might be useful to collate about individuals in order to link the regime to their needs.

The old person's reminiscences then can provide clues as to how the daily routine people are confronted with in a home or hospital can be made as familiar as possible and take into account the personal needs, abilities and preferences of the individual.

SUMMARY

The reminiscences of older people can form the basis for planning:
- outings

which can help to maintain community links.
- displays and exhibitions

which can provide roles for others.

● recreational activities

which can aid in providing meaningful pastimes.

● institutional regimes

which can be tailored to individual needs.

CHAPTER 8

REMINISCENCE WITH THE CONFUSED ELDERLY

*T*he term "confused" is sometimes used to cover a multitude of sins. It is used in many contexts. We can all become confused, for example, after an anaesthetic or too much to drink. After waking up in the morning some of us take many minutes to remember the day, our whereabouts and what we are going to do. Confusion in the elderly may refer to the fact that they wander, they cannot comprehend what is being said to them, they find it difficult to communicate with others easily, they cannot dress themselves or even that they show some kind of inappropriate or bizarre behaviour.

What is "confusion"?

So the first thing we have to establish when thinking about using reminiscence with the confused elderly is exactly what kind of people we wish to work with.

It is important to remember that to describe a person as being "confused" does not explain why they might be behaving in any or all of the ways described above. Confusion is always a symptom of something else, and so, before setting up a reminiscence group, it is also important to ascertain why the people to be involved are confused.

For instance it may be:

● Temporary confusion due to sudden waking, too much drink, anaesthetics, etc.

● Environmental disorientation — being in a strange place or where the person is subject to inaccurate, conflicting or inadequate information from their surroundings.

● Medical states causing a delirium, eg. influenza, cancer, heart disease, toxins, poisons, etc.

● Psychiatric disturbances.

● Metabolic disorders.

● Neurological disorders — tumours, strokes, multiple sclerosis, etc.

● Organic brain syndromes — some of which are treatable, reversible or manageable and some of which are liable to be progressive. Dementia (see below) is one of the signs associated with organic brain syndromes.

Where confusion arises through obviously treatable causes every attempt should be made to see that this is rectified before any thought is given to setting up reminiscence groups.

Confusion and dementia   The term confusion is often used synonymously with "dementia", particularly when organic factors are implicated. However, if someone is described as being demented, it means that they are suffering from a condition which results in a gradual decline of mental functioning. Primary symptoms include loss of memory, disorientation, loss of insight, changes in personality, etc. As we have already said, the term confusion is much more far ranging and may refer to only temporary disruption to mental functioning.

Alzheimer's Disease is the most common type of dementia, but still occurs in only 10% of all people over the age of 65. Alzheimer's Disease is still sometimes called 'senile dementia' but as it is the same in people over and under the age of 65 the word senile is redundant.

Although research is encouraging and new findings are showing the way to improved understanding and possible treatment, as yet no way has been found to halt the dementing process in these progressive diseases. Thus, practically speaking, patients with Alzheimer's Disease and other progressive dementia-related diseases will require long-term care for several years to come. However, in spite of their disability, there will still be things that the sufferer can do and the precise symptoms will differ from individual to individual.

So, the next thing we have to do, having established that the person is confused through a dementia-related state, is to get some idea of what skills and abilities they still retain.

In fact, the main reason why reminiscence is particularly relevant to the confused elderly is because, although memory loss is often very dominant in dementia, it is usually memory for recent events which is lost whilst the ability to remember the past is well preserved.

And so, by its very nature, reminiscence work focuses on the *abilities* of the confused elderly person rather than confronting them with their disability. As further preparation to working with a group of elderly confused people therefore, it may be worthwhile trying to ascertain what other abilities they retain. For instance, someone who has difficulty in finding the right words to describe their feelings or their reminiscences, may be able, by non-verbal gestures, smiles, actions and reactions, to convey quite powerfully the meaning and significance that a particular event has had for them. Similarly, lack of coherent speech does not necessarily imply no ability to comprehend what is said. Therefore, if some sort of skill profile of the person is built up, the reminiscence can be tailored to fit the abilities which are available.

The experience of dementia To help us understand what special considerations we may need to take with confused elderly people it is helpful to have some idea of what confusion can be like for them. Of course we can only guess on the basis of what we know about the abilities which are lost and retained in dementia.

One analogy of the experience of dementia is the feeling that many of us have had when waking up first thing in the morning when we are on holiday: for a split second we find it difficult to remember just where we are and why, until suddenly, it comes back to us. Dementia has been compared to that split-second experience, but the difference is that the person experiences this all of their waking hours. Such an experience can be frightening, bewildering and in some cases can tempt the person to give up or withdraw. The person will find it difficult to make sense of their surroundings and may be desperate to establish some anchor points to help them understand where they are and what is happening to them.

In reminiscence work then, the presentation of stimulus material which is familiar to the confused old person is going to be extremely important. However, it is going to be equally important for them that it is presented in such a way that the person is not going to be confused or bewildered further.

Another difficulty which the old person with dementia is going to have is remembering information for more than a few seconds. This means that after a short while, a question which is asked of them is going to be forgotten, or the reason why someone should put a photograph in front of them is going to be a puzzle unless some explanation is given. Likewise, dementia may mean that the person finds they take much longer to bring to mind relevant information and they are going to be even more frustrated if they feel they are being rushed. How these and other factors can be taken into consideration when engaging in reminiscence work with confused old people is described in more detail in the next section.

Encouraging reminiscence with the confused elderly

Assuming we have ascertained and taken into account why and in what way the person is confused, on the basis of what we assume confusion to be like, we can now put forward some suggestions as to how reminiscence activities might be best encouraged with confused elderly people.

Presenting the right stimulus material

We have already noted how one of the problems for the confused old person is in making sense of his surroundings. Thus we must be sure that they have the best possible opportunity of being able to relate to any stimulus material presented to them. All that we have said in chapter 5 about reminiscence aids applies with particular relevance to the confused elderly.

Thus stimulus material must be:
- clear and unambiguous
- relevant to the individual, their past and

their experiences

● involve the stimulation of as many senses as possible.

Give adequate explanations, cues and prompts

We have already mentioned the effect that short-term memory loss can have on the confused elderly person, so it is important that when the person is introduced to reminiscence work a careful and detailed explanation of what is happening is given. Likewise, the confused old person may need to have stimulus material described to them or have relevant aspects pointed out to them in a specific way. More specific prompting or questioning may be necessary with confused elderly people in order to help them give an appropriate response, eg. "What did you do in the war?" may be too general a question. A more appropriate question might be, "What job did you do in the war?" or, using relevant stimulus material, "What do you think that person is doing? Have you done this sort of thing?"

It may be that the confused old person needs some help in finding the right response or reply. For instance, they may need help in finding the right words by being given a start with one or two relevant cues.

It is important to be sensitive to how the person is coping with the situation. It is all too easy to take over when it is not necessary. Not providing sufficient help is another common error in practice.

Encourage any responses evoked

For confused elderly people the problem is going to be evoking any response at all. Therefore it is important to encourage any response at all rather than to be concerned too much about the exact nature of the response. It has been mentioned that historical accuracy is less important than personal recall of experiences. Again this is of particular importance with confused elderly people. Once an initial response has been evoked, where appropriate, it may then be possible to shape or cue the reminiscer towards more specific and/or extended responses.

Use non-verbal reactions

In chapter 1 we saw that people do not have to talk about their past to be reminiscing. Sometimes memories are recalled privately. This possibility should be borne in mind, especially with confused elderly people who may not be able to verbalise their thoughts and feelings, but who nevertheless still experience them just as intensely. The job of the reminiscence facilitator is to be aware of how feelings can be expressed through non-verbal reactions such as eye gaze, expression on the face, posture or even tone and inflexion of the voice. Awareness of this kind of communication can help to give the facilitator an indication of what themes might be of particular relevance to the individual with whom he is working.

Be flexible about pace

With confused elderly people there is more of a danger that they will be subject to over stimulation or excessive demand on their abilities rather than the opposite. It is important to give the confused elderly person time to absorb questions or stimulus materials and also to respond to them in whatever way they are able. Valuable responses can be lost if priority is given to getting through a session or a set of stimulus materials rather than giving time for the old person to give of themselves.

Probably the biggest trap people working with the confused elderly can fall into is that of making unrealistic expectations as to what can be achieved with them. Reminiscence work with confused elderly people is unlikely to be as easy, spontaneous or dramatic as with groups of other old people. It can, however, be just as rewarding if the level of expectation is moderated. For instance, it is worth remembering that someone suffering with a dementia-related state is experiencing a progressive decline in mental

Levels of expectation

functioning. Therefore, quite apart from looking for improvements, anything which can help to halt or moderate the rate of decline can be seen as a substantial achievement. In practical terms, to hold the attention of a confused old person who spends most of their day wandering around the ward mumbling incoherently, for 10 seconds, can be seen as a remarkable achievement when compared with what would otherwise be the norm for that person.

Reminiscence groups with confused old people may require a lot more input and energy from the leader but if achievements are measured in relation to the needs and abilities of the participants substantial changes can be observed. Reminiscence on a one-to-one basis, where stimulus material can more easily be geared to the individual, provides the most flexible situation in which to work with confused elderly people. However, reminiscence with confused elderly people in any situation is best achieved when the level of activity and expectation is tailored to the needs and abilities of the participants.

SUMMARY
Before setting up reminiscence work with confused elderly people it is important:
- to identify and eliminate causes of confusion
- to obtain a profile of what abilities the confused person has.

Reminiscence work with confused elderly people should ensure:
- presentation of the right material
- adequate explanation, cues and prompts
- encouragement of all responses
- use of non-verbal reactions
- flexibility

It is important that achievements are measured in relation to the needs and abilities of confused old people.

CHAPTER 9

EFFECTS OF REMINISCENCE
FOR THE CARERS

So far we have examined the impact that reminiscing can have on the lives of elderly people. However there can also be benefits in encouraging reminiscence for those who work with and care for the elderly. Just as the old person can gain in self-esteem and a sense of identity through sharing their wisdom and experience, so the interested listener can gain a deeper insight into the lives of those they care for. Instead of being just another mouth to feed or body to dress, the old person becomes a human being with a unique and individual past, lifestyle and background. In listening to the old person the carer can become more aware of the characteristics, whims and idiosyncrasies that go towards defining the person as an individual. The listener can also learn a great deal from the old person's store of memories.

Broadly speaking then, reminiscence can help to increase the interface between the old person and his carer. Reminiscence provides the framework in which the carer can get to know the old person better, so allowing for more meaningful contact between them.

The significance of the impact of this aspect of reminiscence on the carer should not be underestimated. It is not unusual to find difficulty in recruiting professional staff to work with elderly people. One of the reasons often given for this is that staff find it hard to grasp the purpose of working with older people and are unable to identify the rewards and job satisfaction that can be gained. Highlighting reminiscence as a distinctive contribution which old people can make and the benefits which can be derived in both sharing and listening to the memories can help to dispel this myth.

Recognising reminiscence as an important part of the process of adapting to old age can also help the carer to appreciate the value of giving time and space to listen to the elderly person talking about their past. All too often the physical tasks of bathing, washing, feeding, etc can hinder the establishment of a proper relationship between carer and old person. A reminiscence framework gives licence to carers and staff to spend time listening to what people have to say and puts this kind of activity in the context of improving the old person's quality of life. Just as important, it can allow the caring task to take on a more human face and the reminiscence process can engender a sense of purpose in working with the elderly and hence improve job satisfaction and staff morale. For the carer at home too, it may be important that there is a recognition of the status of the old person's past in relation to their present. For instance, it may make it more bearable to put up with repeated stories from the past if the carer knows that sharing memories serves a worthwhile function for the reminiscer.

A further benefit for the carer of encouraging and acknowledging the old person's reminiscences is that it may stimulate further interest in that person which can have all kinds of implications for other areas of their lives, as described in chapter 6.

One useful framework in helping the carer get to know the old person in more depth is presented in Appendix IV. This resident's profile identifies some of the key areas relating to the past and experiences of the individual which may be of value in generating ideas for other reminiscence-based activities. These profiles can also act as a basis for care planning exercises where it is vital to take into account the background and lifestyle of the old person when considering what might be realistic objectives for the care of that individual.

Any activity which improves the quality of life for the old person and their contact with others must be worthwhile. Reminiscence is of particular value in that, whilst doing this, the dignity of the old person is maintained and their self-esteem is enhanced. At the same time the listener can gain from the experiences which are shared and the depth of insight gained with the elderly person as an individual.

SUMMARY
For the carer, reminiscence can aid in:
- helping in the appreciation of the elderly person as an individual
- learning from the old person's store of memories
- improving the interface with the old person
- improving morale and job satisfaction.

CHAPTER 10

THEORETICAL PERSPECTIVES

Throughout this book we have tried to highlight the positive contribution that reminiscence work can make to the lives of elderly people and those who care for them. We have described the role that reminiscence has to play in meeting the emotional, social and psychological needs of the elderly and how it may help the person to come to terms with and adapt to old age. Reminiscing is a process in which the old person becomes engaged — sometimes by themselves, sometimes with others. Much of our emphasis has been on public reminiscing where the role of an interested listener has been important. In these situations, much of the value of reminiscence is gained through the interaction and interface created between reminiscer and listener. Reminiscing acts as a framework within which the two can be brought together and provides an essential link between the emotional life of an old person and the people with whom he comes into contact. Most importantly, however, public reminiscing is a unique kind of interaction which relies on the resources and information which the old person chooses to bring to bear in his relationship with others rather than having to rely on their initiatives.

The reminiscence philosophy

Encouraging and facilitating reminiscence does not rely on operating a defined set of techniques. Rather it depends on establishing the right balance in the relationship between reminiscer and listener, and in creating an atmosphere of respect and genuine interest for the old person as an individual, as someone who has something to offer.

We have also described how the effect of reminiscing can go beyond the verbal exchange. Indeed reminiscing can almost take on the status of a caring philosophy in which the individual's past, background and lifestyle form the basis on which care is provided. This philosophy emphasises the assets and abilities of the elderly and the positive contribution they can make. We have illustrated how aspects of the old person's life such as mealtimes, daily routine, recreational activities, etc can all be perceived in terms of this kind of philosophy.

Some misconceptions

Reminiscence has not always been viewed in a positive way. Indeed, when attention was first focused on the reminiscences of elderly people, the frequency with which they talked about the past was seen as part of a pathological ageing process. The view was that old people focus on the past as a way of escaping from the present because they cannot take on board change. It was only when Robert Butler's life review process was conceptualised as part of human development in later life by Erik Erikson that people began to see the potential benefits of encouraging reminiscing.

In fact this conceptualisation helped to explain why the quality and nature of people's reminiscences differ. McMahon and Rhudick (1967) were able to identify four kinds of reminiscence. The first group were those who seem to take great pleasure in sharing their past. This group comprised those who had successfully adapted to old age. In contrast, the other three groups, whose reminiscences were characterised by over-exaggeration, anxiety and guilt or withdrawal and blocking respectively, represented people who, for various reasons, were unable to accept or come to terms with their age. Reminiscence was thus seen as having a possible positive contribution to make in helping the adjustment to old age.

Another misconception which has arisen over reminiscence is that it encourages people to live in the past. However, although the content of reminiscence refers to the past the actual *process* of reminiscing involves a *current* interaction between the old person and his interested listener. Therefore the benefits of reminiscing lie in the immediate effect that it has upon the interface between the old person and his listener rather than what is said. Moreover it is often worth considering what alternatives or substitutes are provided with respect to an old person's past accomplishments and achievements. After all, there are many elderly people in long-term care who are condemned to spending the rest of their lives locked in geriatric chairs and trying to battle with their deteriorating physical and mental faculties. In this context reminiscing can be seen as a positive response to coping with and adjusting to the problems of old age.

We have already considered the issues relating to the ethics of resurrecting memories which might be upsetting to the elderly person. Expressed in its most extreme form, reminiscence might be seen as dangerous. Of course it has to be admitted that not all memories are happy ones and indeed it is only right that if an old person's reminiscences are to reflect the richness and variety of his past life then this should be so. However, the anxiety of uncovering unhappy memories can often reside as much with the listener as with the old person. As we have suggested, reminiscence may generate the material for the life review process which helps in adaptation to old age and death.

Finally there has been some concern expressed that the values explicit in reminiscence work are contradictory to the principles of reality orientation where the emphasis is placed on keeping the old person in touch with the present. However, like reality orientation, reminiscing, particularly with confused elderly people, has provided a framework in which people can feel comfortable about interacting with the elderly. Reminiscence possibly has the advantage over reality orientation in that its principles and values are rather more easy to identify with. Nevertheless, inherent in the reality orientation approach is an attempt to help the old person relate to their environment — both physical and social. If talking about the past helps the old person to maintain relationships with people in that environment then the objectives are fulfilled. Indeed, in many reality orientation sessions reminiscence-type activities form an integral part of the programme.

Conclusions

Because reminiscence is a natural process in which most of us participate from time to time, it forms a framework within which anyone can feel at ease. At the very least therefore reminiscence-based work has provided a means by which the contact between elderly people and others has been increased in quantity and quality. More than that, reminiscence work offers the opportunity to recognise old people as individuals who have something positive to contribute to life. It may also provide the old person with a means of adapting to later life.

Reminiscence work can be exploited in a huge variety of ways, each of which has its own rewards for elderly people and those who work with and care for them. However rewards are only there if we give ourselves the opportunity to experience them.

Happy Reminiscing!

Appendix I

Sample Programme for a Reminiscence Group

Session 1: ***Names*** *Where participants have lived*
The changes that have taken place over the years

Session 2: ***Occupations*** *What jobs entail*
Why they chose that job

Session 3: ***The Family*** *How many and who*
Where are they now
Family favourites

Session 4: ***Hobbies and Interests*** *Membership of clubs etc*

Session 5: ***Important Events*** *The happiest time(s) in their lives*
The saddest time(s) in their lives
The circumstances involved

Session 6: ***Leisure Activities*** *How spare time was spent*

Session 7: ***Holidays*** *Where, when and how often*
What they used to do

Session 8: ***Wartime activities*** *Where they were and what they were doing*

Session 8: ***Royalty*** *Who they remember and what*

Session 10: ***Points of Progress*** *Innovations they have witnessed*
The effect of change on their lives

Session 11: ***Schooling*** *Favourite and disliked subjects*
Level attained, length of time

Session 12: ***Famous events*** *eg. Coronation, D-day etc*

APPENDIX II

Suggestions for Reminiscence Stimulus Materials

Old photographs
Postcards
Comics
Museum objects
Personal mementos
Food packaging
Recipe books

Archive materials
Old records
Old films
Personal life history books.
Sporting equipment
Ration books
Slides

Videos
Television programmes
Radio programmes
Local history books
Clothing
Furniture
Games

APPENDIX III

Reminiscence Resource Materials

1. Nostalgia: a series of stimulus cards

a) Then & Now – Objects

b) Then & Now – Vehicles

c) Banner Headlines

d) Royalty

e) Bygone Decades series

f) Memory Diary

Available from Winslow Press, 9 London Lane, London E8 3PR.

Memory Joggers: a series of photographs relating to the past.

Published by CREATA. Available from Winslow Press, 9 London Lane, London E8 3PR.

2. Recall: a series of tape/slide sequences of scenes from London over the past 80 years

a) Childhood

b) Youth

c) The First World War

d) Living through the Thirties

e) The second World War

f) A Different World

Available from Help the Aged, 16-18 St James' Walk, Clerkenwell, London EC1R OBE.

3. Reminiscence and Recall: a video training film on how to run reminiscence groups.

Available from Help the Aged, 16-18 St James' Walk, Clerkenwell, London EC1R OBE.

APPENDIX IV

Profile Sheet

Name: _____ How person likes to be addressed: _____

Age: _____ Date of birth: _____

Place of Origin: _____ Places of special significance: _____

Schooling (where and how much): _____

_____

_____

Occupation(s): _____

_____

_____

Hobbies and Interests: _____

_____

_____

Church attended: _____

Marital status: _____ Significant others: _____

Children: _____ Grandchildren: _____

Important Values/Beliefs: _____

_____

Particular Likes/Dislikes: _____

_____

Personality: _____

_____

Other significant information: _____

_____

_____

_____

_____

Reminiscence Group Observation Chart

Session No: _____ Leader(s): _____

Theme: _____ Date: _____

Rate each group member on a 0-4 scale according to how they perform on the dimensions described below:

0 = poor response
1 = slight response
2 = fair response
3 = good response
4 = excellent response

Dimensions	Group Members' Initials								
Attentiveness *(degree to which appeared interested in group)*									
Responsiveness *(degree to which participant responds to the stimulus material, discussion or prompting)*									
Spontaneity *(degree to which participant offers contribution of his/her own accord)*									
Involvement *(non-verbal response to group activity)*									
Individual Score Totals									
							Group Total		

Calculate the Individual Score Totals for each participant by adding the scores on each dimension for each group member. Calculate the Group Total by adding the Individual Score.

APPENDIX VI

Further Reading

Butler, R.N., 'The life review. An interpretation of reminiscence in the aged',
Psychiatry, 26, 65-76, 1963

Erikson, E., *Childhood and Society*, W.W. Norton & Co., New York, 1950

Kiernat, J.M., 'The use of life review activity with confused nursing home residents',
American Journal of Occupational Therapy, 33, 306-10, 1979

McMahon, A.W. and Rhudick, P.J., 'Reminiscing in the aged: an adaptational response',
in Lewis, S., & Kaherd, R. (eds.), *Psychodynamic Studies of Aging*, International Universities Press,
New York, 1967

Merriam, S., 'The concept and function of reminiscence: A review of the research',
Gerontologist, 20, (5), 604-8, 1980

Norris, A.D. & Abu El Eileh, N., 'Reminiscing — A therapy for both elderly patients and their
staff', *Nursing Times*, 78, 32, 1368-9, 1982